MATH:
A RICH HERITAGE

Product Development

Beatrice Lumpkin

Arthur B. Powell

Consultants

Claudia Zaslavsky

Freddie Renfro

Charlotte Samuels

GLOBE FEARON EDUCATIONAL PUBLISHER

Executive Editor: Barbara Levadi
Project Editor: Carol Schneider
Editor: Kirsten Richert
Product Development:
   Beatrice Lumpkin, Associate Professor of Mathematics,
      retired, Malcolm X College of the Chicago City Colleges
   Arthur B. Powell, Associate Professor of Mathematics,
      Rutgers University, Newark, New Jersey
Consultants: Claudia Zaslavsky, author of *Africa Counts, Fear of Math*, and *The Multicultural Math Classroom*
   Freddie Renfro, Director of Mathematics, Goose Creek
      School District, Houston, Texas
   Charlotte Samuels, Mathematics Consultant and Teacher,
      Roxborough High School, Philadelphia, Pennsylvania
Marketing Manager: Nancy Surridge
Art Direction and Design: Joan Jacobus
Art and Photo Research: Jenifer Hixson
Production Director: Penny Gibson
Production Editor: Rosann Bar
Electronic Page Production: Joan Jacobus, José López, and
   Elaine Kilcullen
Maps: Mapping Specialists
Cover Design: Joan Jacobus

Globe Fearon Educational Publisher wishes to thank the following copyright owners for permission to reproduce illustrations and photographs in this book:

p. 1 (top): Eric Lessing from Art Resource; p.1 (center): The Granger Collection; p.1 (right): The Granger Collection; p.1 (bottom): Giraudon/Art Resource; p. 2 (top): The Granger Collection; p. 2 (bottom): The Granger Collection; p. 3 (top): The Granger Collection; p. 3 (top right): The Bettmann Archive; p. 3 (bottom right): The Granger Collection; p. 4: The Granger Collection; p. 4 (top insert): Scala/Art Resource; p. 4 (bottom insert): The Granger Collection; p. 6: Art Resource; p. 8 (left):

Photo credits continued on inside back cover.

Printed in the United States of America
2 3 4 5 6 7 8 9 10   96 97 98 99 00

ISBN: 0-8359-1833-5

BA8

GLOBE FEARON EDUCATIONAL PUBLISHER
A Division of Simon & Schuster
Upper Saddle River, New Jersey

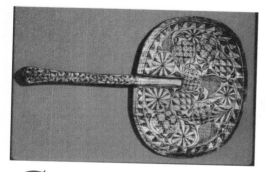

Contents

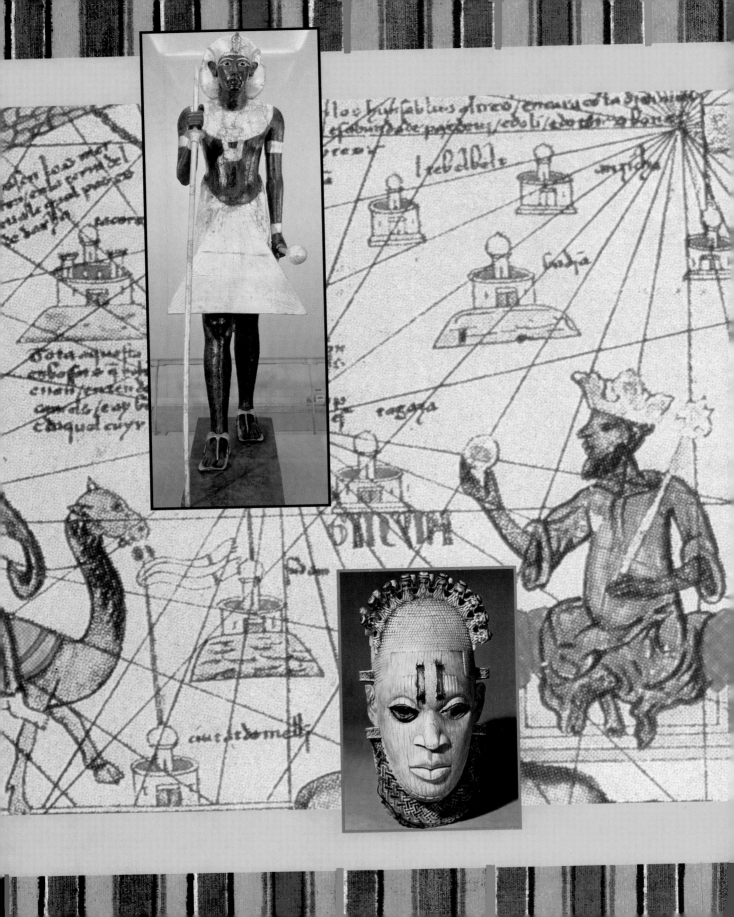

MATH: A RICH HERITAGE

Do you think that math doesn't matter to you? If you do, you may be interested to know that the workplace of the future requires employees to be able to think, solve problems, and communicate using mathematical concepts. Most jobs today involve some degree of math. Mathematics, for example, is the foundation of science, engineering, and technology—and it is an important element in everyday life.

Regardless of your career interests, you should study math throughout your school career. In high school, you can choose the math courses you will take. You can choose to take consumer math or general math. However, these classes may not help your future. Or, you can choose to take the academic, or advanced, math courses. These classes are known as the "gatekeeper courses" because they are required for entrance to college. They are also essential for the better-paying jobs.

This book can help you determine the role math will play in your life. You will explore the African roots of modern mathematics. You will also discover how math influenced the contributions and achievements of several African Americans in math-related careers. Finally, you will examine the goals of various math courses offered in school and how these courses provide access to higher education and the best-paying careers.

Everyone can succeed in math. Choose your courses wisely. Expand your opportunities.

▲ *The Egyptian god Osiris sits on his throne in the Land of the Dead.*

The African Heritage of Math

MATH BEGINS IN AFRICA.

According to most scientists, the first people lived in Africa. There, people first developed language, tools, and organized ways of living. People also created **mathematics**. Mathematics is the use of numbers, shapes, and patterns to describe and explain the world.

Early Evidence of Math In Africa, scientists found early evidence of people's use of math. A fossil bone was discovered in Zaire (see map of present-day Africa on page 47), at a place now called Ishango. This bone is about 25,000 years old. It has many **tallies**, or marks, that represent number counts.

Some scientists think the Ishango bone was a calendar. Others think it shows that people had discovered multiplication. The tallies for 3 and 6, 4 and 8, and for 5 and 10, could show people were multiplying by 2. Although the meaning of the Ishango bone is unknown, it shows mathematical thinking.

Tallies are one way to write numbers. People use tallies to count days or objects. But there is a problem with using tallies to record numbers. How large a number could you easily write and read, using tally marks? Recording large numbers with tallies is not practical. It takes too much time, and tallies are difficult to read. So people came up with a new way to record numbers. In 3100 BCE, Africans in the Nile Valley invented numerals.

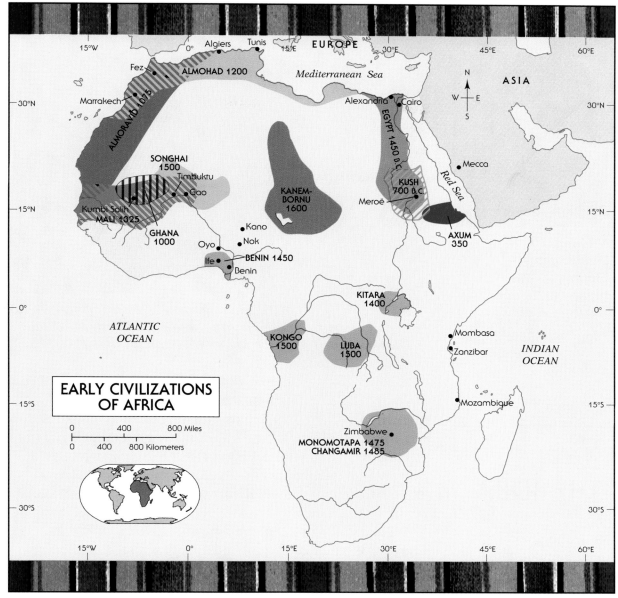

EARLY CIVILIZATIONS
OF AFRICA

| 0 | 400 | 800 Miles |
| 0 | 400 | 800 Kilometers |

ANCIENT EGYPTIANS DEVELOP MATH.

Over 6,000 years ago, Africans farmed the Nile Valley.
Each year, the Nile River flooded. When it receded, it
left rich soil in the valley. Farmers grew many crops
after the flood, especially grain. When a flood was
high, farmers grew enough grain. But some years the
flood waters were too low to reach all of the
farmland. Then many people starved.

▲ *This map shows
some of the great
cultures and
civilizations that arose
in Africa. Africans
created vast trade
networks. This trade
spread products and
ideas among Africa,
Asia, and Europe.*

7

▲ *This scribe, Amenhotep (1460 to 1380 BCE), was also an architect. He designed beautiful temples for his pharaoh.*

▲ *An official measures a field of grain while the farmer and his wife watch. Below, scribes count the grain harvest. This wall painting is from the scribe Mennah's tomb around 1500 BCE.*

EXPLORE THE IDEA
▼

A surviving Egyptian record lists the height of the Nile flood for each year from about 2500 to 1900 BCE. What do you think scribes could learn by keeping this record?

▲▲▲▲▲▲▲▲▲▲

To keep people from starving, Africans in the Nile River Valley began to store grain. They organized farming, storage, and distribution. Over time, this organization led to the first central government. This government was called Egypt. Egypt was ruled by a pharaoh, or king. In good years, the pharaoh saved extra grain. In years with low flood waters, he gave grain to the people.

The pharaoh employed many scribes, or clerks. They kept track of the amount of grain stored. Scribes also recorded how high the Nile flooded each year. Taxes were based on crop sizes, which were determined by floods.

Inventing Numerals Over time, the number of people in the Nile Valley rose to 3 million. That was too large a number for scribes to record with tallies. So these Africans made a great breakthrough.

They still used tallies for numbers one through nine. But for 10, they used a symbol to stand for ten tallies. (**||||||||||** = **∩**) For 11, the scribes wrote **∩I**, and for 12, **∩II**, and so on. They invented more symbols to write numbers up to 1,000,000. This invention made it easy to use large numbers. Modern numerals use this African idea of symbols, instead of tallies.

A System of Measures To figure out fair exchanges, ancient Egyptians created a system of measurements. They used the length of a forearm to measure cloth. They called this length a cubit. But whose arm should be used? A short arm was good for the seller. But if you were the buyer, wouldn't you want a long arm? To make a trade, buyer and seller had to agree on the length of the cubit. Egyptians set the cubit as the length of the forearm of a pharaoh. The cubit was now a standard length.

Ancient Egyptians also created fractions. To measure fractions of a cubit, they used palms and fingers. Four fingers equalled one palm, and seven palms was one cubit. For fine measures, fingers were divided into halves, thirds, fourths, and so on.

Studying the Stars Egypt depended on the annual Nile flood. Everyone watched for the date of the flood. Egyptian astronomers studied the skies. They saw stars in the north that stayed in place during the night. Other stars seemed to cross the sky from east to west. Astronomers used the fixed stars in the north to

EXPLORE THE IDEA
▼▼

How many 4-finger palms are there in your personal cubit? Measure with 4 fingers from elbow to middle fingertip of your arm. Compare with others in your class. The royal cubit was equal to 7 palms. What does that tell you about the pharaoh who set the standard? Was he tall or short?

▲▲▲▲▲▲▲▲▲▲
▼▼▼▼▼▼▼▼▼

▲ *Egyptian astronomers made careful records of their observations. In 1080 BCE, the night and day journey of the sun was painted on the ceiling of the tomb of Pharaoh Ramses VI.*

▲ *This water clock was one invention that Egyptians used to measure time.*

EXPLORE THE IDEA ▼

In Egyptian numerals, ⟨ replaced 100 tally strokes. For 600, Egyptians wrote ⟨⟨⟨⟨⟨⟨, instead of 600 strokes. Compare the Egyptian way and the modern way of writing one hundred and six hundred. What are the advantages and disadvantages of both systems?

find the four directions—north, east, south, west. They used other stars to find the hour of the night.

The most important star for these astronomers was the bright star Sirius (SIHR-ee-uhs). Sirius disappears for part of the year. It comes back at dawn on the day the Nile begins to flood. This happens exactly once in 365 days. So Egyptians made the first calendar with 365 days in a year. They were also the first to use a 24-hour day, with 12 equal hours of day and night.

Geometry and the Pyramids Although the Nile floods were needed to grow crops, they also washed away farm boundaries. To redraw these boundaries, Egyptians created **geometry**. Geometry is mathematics that deals with points, lines, planes, and shapes and their measurement and relationships in space. The Egyptians invented geometry formulas for area and volume. We learn these same formulas in school today. The Egyptian formula for the area of a circle was 99.4 percent accurate, the best in the ancient world.

Geometry was used to plan the **pyramids**. A pyramid is a structure with a square base and four triangular sides that meet at a point. Egyptians built huge pyramids as tombs for their pharaohs. Building such a large structure was very difficult. Egyptian mathematicians used advanced equations to get these structures right. Scientists today are amazed at how perfect the pyramids are. The corner angles of the Great Pyramid are accurate to 1/3000 of a degree!

Making the First Graph Construction projects, such as pyramids, led Egyptians to another breakthrough. At the Saqqara (suh-KAHR-uh) step pyramid, scientists found a plan for a curved roof. This pyramid was next to a temple with a curved roof that matched the plan. The plan gives numbers for the height and the distance of points on the curve. Mathematicians call these numbers **coordinates**. They use coordinates to plot points in a plane to make lines and curves. Until this plan was found, historians thought that coordinates were invented in Europe. Today we know that coordinates were an African invention, dating back to 2700 BCE in Egypt.

Using Zero Egyptians also created an idea similar to zero. To support the pyramids' great weight, architects had to build deep foundations. They needed a way to measure heights above and below ground. So they created numbers similar to positive and negative integers. These are the numbers we write as ". . . -2, -1, 0, 1, 2. . . ."

Egyptian architects drew lines parallel to the ground to guide construction. They labeled the line at ground level zero. Lines above ground were marked 1 cubit above zero, 2 cubits above zero, and so on. Lines below ground were marked 1 cubit below zero, 2 cubits below zero, and so on.

Egyptians also used zero in bookkeepers' records. An account book from 1700 BCE has the earliest example of zero used as an answer to a problem. Bookkeepers recorded the supplies that the royal family used. In the columns for ducks, oil, and fruit, all supplies that came in, went out to the cooks. Three columns can still be read: 7 - 7 = 0, 52 - 52 = 0, 200 - 200 = 0. The use of zero was a very important discovery.

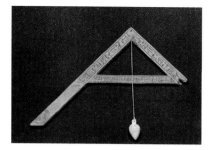

▲ *Egyptian architects used this tool, the square and plumb-line, to help them build the pyramids.*

▲ *The calculations that Egyptian architects used were so exact that the pyramids at Giza still stand today. Scientists estimate that 100,000 people built the pyramids during the floods of the Nile River.*

▲ *Alexandria was the center of a vast trading network. Ships brought Egyptian ideas, as well as grain, cloth, and gold, to other lands.*

GREAT EMPIRES AND CULTURES GROW AND CHANGE.

Through trading, warfare, and travel, Egyptians and their ideas came in contact with many peoples. Egyptian discoveries in mathematics spread far into the Middle East, Europe, and throughout Africa. Other peoples expanded on these Egyptian ideas.

Alexandria, Queen City of Science Egypt's wealth was attractive to invaders. In 332 BCE, the Greek army of Alexander the Great conquered Egypt. Alexander built a new capital city of Egypt called Alexandria.

For 700 years, Alexandria was known as the Queen City of Science. Egyptian mathematicians worked with mathematicians from what is now Greece, Libya, Italy, and Turkey. Based on their work, Euclid (YOO-klihd) of Alexandria wrote *Geometry*. This book on higher mathematics is studied even today. The famous astronomer Ptolemy (TAHL-uh-mee) was also from Alexandria. His book on astronomy was called "the greatest" for 1000 years. Another African mathematician, Eratosthenes (ehr-uh-TAHS-thuh-nees), was from what is now Libya. He was the first to find the earth's circumference.

▲ *The people of Axum erected massive stone structures. This tall monument looks like a modern skyscraper.*

Alexandria was also the home of Hypatia (HIH-paht-EE-uh), the first woman mathematician whose name is known. She was a famous professor at the University of Alexandria. In 415 CE, Hypatia was murdered. She was torn apart by a mob who opposed her beliefs. Some historians say this horrible event marked the end of Alexandria's leadership in science. But it was not the end of mathematics in Africa.

Kush and Axum Kush was a powerful kingdom to the south of Egypt. While Egypt was under Greek rule, Kush remained independent. Around 540 BCE, Kushites built a new capital at Meroe (MEHR-uh-way). Science and technology reached a high level there. Kushite drawings show astronomers studying the stars. Hills of iron waste prove that Meroe was a huge iron-smelting center. Kush may have been in contact with the Nok people in West Africa and other African iron-producing centers. (See map on page 7.)

For 700 years, Meroe ruled the region. Then Axum (AK-soom), in what is now Ethiopia, became the most powerful. It was a great center of trade. Merchants sold ivory and gold to Greek, Persian, and Indian traders. The people of Axum developed their own schools and system of writing. The churches of Axum were carved into solid rock. Some of these great churches still stand today.

Islamic Mathematics in Africa In 642 CE, an Arab army conquered Egypt and swept across much of Africa. Afterward, North Africa became a great center of learning. Egyptians built a science center, known as the "House of Wisdom," in Cairo.

Arabic became the language of science. Jews and Christians, as well as Muslims, wrote mathematics books in Arabic. Abu Kamil (AH-boo KAH-mihl) wrote about algebra. Ibn Yunus (IHB-uhn YOO-nuhs) wrote about trigonometry and astronomy. These books were carried from North Africa to Europe. Europeans used them to study advanced mathematics.

Through trade with North Africa, Europeans learned Indo-Arabic numerals. The numerals, 1 to 9

EXPLORE THE IDEA
▼

Why were there few women mathematicians in Hypatia's time? Why do you think more women are studying mathematics today?

▲▲▲▲▲▲▲▲▲▲

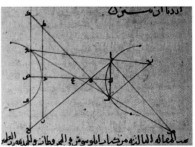

▲ *Ibn al-Haytham (965–1039 CE) experimented with light and vision. This sketch shows how he used math to study light.*

13
▼▼

EXPLORE THE IDEA
▼

Why do you think we use Indo-Arabic numerals today, instead of Roman numerals? (Hint: the Roman numeral for 724 is DCCXXIV.)

▲▲▲▲▲▲▲▲▲▲

▲ *The Great Mosque at Kairouan, in what is now Tunisia, is one of the oldest Islamic buildings in North Africa. It was built in 670 CE.*

and 0, were invented in India. Then Islamic mathematicians, writing in Arabic, added decimal numerals. Indo-Arabic numerals are used by most people in the world today.

Islamic learning also spread to West Africa. This time, contact with Islamic ideas came through trade. Muslims were attracted by West Africa's rich civilization. By 1000 CE, a great trading empire had grown there. This was the Empire of Ghana.

The Riches of West Africa The Empire of Ghana ruled West Africa for hundreds of years. Its wealth came from agriculture, crafts, and control of the gold and salt trade. Ghana was more powerful than most

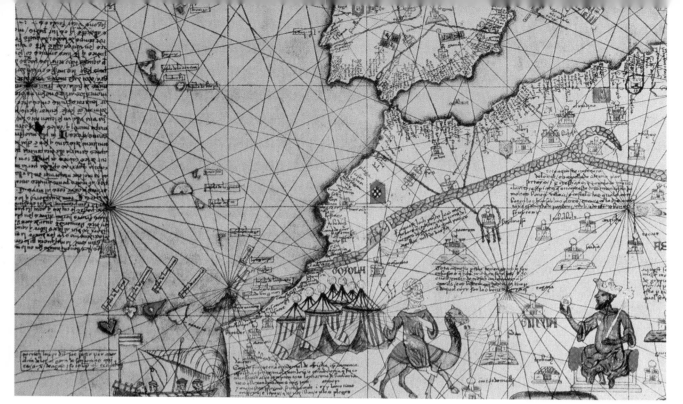

▲ *On this European map created in 1375, the figure of Mansa Musa represents Mali. He is seated on a throne with a gold crown.*

European countries of that time. Ghana's army was huge. It was several times larger than the Norman army that conquered England in 1066. Ghanian mathematicians kept track of the army, set taxes, and helped control trade.

By 1223, Ghana was replaced by Mali. This was an even larger West African empire. Mali controlled 500,000 square miles. Mali's important trading cities were Gao (GAH-oh) and Timbuktu (tihm-buhk-TOO).

Mali's greatest ruler was Mansa Musa (MAHN-suh MOO-suh). He was a Muslim. In 1324, he made a pilgrimage to Mecca. The size and wealth of his caravan amazed all who saw it. Mansa Musa brought with him 60,000 men and 30,000 pounds of gold. Mansa Musa spent so much gold in Cairo that the price of gold dropped. After this trip, word of Mali's wealth spread across the world.

Mali declined after Mansa Musa's death. Then the Empire of Songhai (sahng-HY) came into power. Timbuktu was also its center. Under the Songhai

EXPLORE THE IDEA
▼

The ancient map above shows Mansa Musa wearing a golden crown. This was the first European map of West Africa. Why do you think Mansa Musa appears on this map?

▲▲▲▲▲▲▲▲▲▲

▲ *Gold trade played a key part in the empires and cultures of West Africa. These small weights were used by the Akan people, in what is now Ghana and Côte d'Ivoire, to measure gold dust. This is one of many systems of measurement developed in West Africa.*

▲ *Islam's finest architects and scholars helped enlarge and enrich Timbuktu. This European drawing from 1830, however, shows little of the city's glory.*

Empire, this great city reached its golden age. Timbuktu's university became world famous. From all over Africa, students came to study law, religion, and the sciences. The Arab historian Hamman Ibn Muhammad (HAHM-mahn IHB-uhn MOO-hah-mhed) wrote: "In Timbuktu, there are many judges, doctors, and clerics [priests]. All these positions receive good salaries from the king. He pays great respect to men of learning."

Enslaved in the Americas In the late 1400s, Portuguese sailors landed in West Africa. This led to great changes for African peoples. The most significant change was the growth of the slave trade.

Hundreds of thousands of Africans were sold to Portuguese and other European traders. These Africans were packed into slave ships. They were brought across the Atlantic Ocean. Many died on the voyage. Those who survived were enslaved in the Americas.

Despite slavery, these Africans kept alive their cultures. Many African Americans today are continuing the African tradition of excellence in mathematics. Their interesting stories can be models for your future.

Achievements in Math

▲ *Sculptor Augusta Savage (1900–1962) used her excellent sense of ratio and proportion to create a realistic style.*

Throughout history, African Americans have contributed to the field of math and to math-related careers. In the 19th century, before the end of slavery in 1863, African Americans educated themselves in reading, writing, and arithmetic, or mathematics. You will read about one such person—Benjamin Banneker, a self-taught mathematician and astronomer. Although Lewis Latimer was born free, he was also born during slavery. You will learn that despite prejudice, Latimer became a well-known and respected inventor.

African Americans have continued their tradition of excellence in mathematics in the 20th century. In this section, you will also read about the life stories of several prominent African Americans in math-related fields. Their stories are told here to encourage all students to prepare for the challenges of the 21st century and beyond.

▲ *Scientist George Washington Carver (1864–1943) vastly changed agriculture in the South. Carver earned a Master's Degree in science at a time when high school diplomas were rare. Here, Carver teaches chemistry at Tuskegee Institute.*

Benjamin Banneker (1731–1806)

Mathematician, Astronomer

Washington, D.C., is a symbol of freedom in the Western world. Yet, it was built with the help of an African American man in a time when slavery was common in this country. Benjamin Banneker was born in Baltimore County, Maryland, in 1731. He is the best-known African American mathematician from the early days of the United States. He overcame the barriers of race, age, and a lack of formal education to become a noted astronomer.

Banneker's grandfather, Bannaka, was born the son of an African king. He was kidnapped by slave traders and brought to America. In Maryland, Bannaka was sold to Molly Welsh, an Englishwoman. Welsh freed Bannaka, and in time they were married. Their oldest daughter, Mary, also married a freed slave. Her husband, Robert, took Bannaka's name as his last name. He changed the spelling of this name to Banneker. When Robert and Mary had their first child, they named him Benjamin.

Benjamin Banneker learned how to read from his grandmother Molly and how to do simple math from a local Quaker teacher. At an early age, Banneker showed his skill in mathematics. Later in life, he taught himself, using books that he had borrowed. Through his own efforts, Banneker became well-educated in a time when few people were.

Banneker's first taste of fame came at the age of 22, when he built a clock from drawings that he made of a pocket watch. Banneker looked at the project as a mathematical problem. He carefully worked out the ratios of the gears and wheels, and drew each part to scale. Then he whittled the clock works from wood. That clock kept time faithfully. People came from far and wide to see it. Overnight, Banneker was a celebrity.

For 36 years after he built the clock, Banneker worked on his farm. He had few books to study but continued to be a clever observer. Banneker wanted to study the movements of the stars and planets. At last, at the age of 57, he got his chance. It started when a friend loaned him some astronomy books, a telescope, and a compass. "I'll come back and show you how to use them," he promised. Banneker could not wait. Before long, he had mastered astronomy and complex mathematics. Banneker became so interested in astronomy that he watched the stars all night and recorded what he saw in his journal.

Banneker's knowledge of astronomy led to his greatest honor. In 1791, he was asked to help survey the new nation's capital, Washington, D.C. A **surveyor** measures the size, shape, and boundaries of a piece of land with special equipment. It was not an easy job for a sixty-year-old man. The six-man team worked and slept out in the cold and rain, traveling through hills and swamps. Banneker, however, considered it his greatest adventure.

After his return from Washington, Banneker published several **almanacs**—books that forecast weather, as well as moon, sun, and tide movements. Farmers and sailors used this information.

Banneker sent a copy of his first almanac to Thomas Jefferson, the Secretary of State at that time. He asked Jefferson to judge the book on its own value before noting the skin color of its author. In his reply to Banneker, Jefferson wrote that Banneker's talents were equal to those of "other colors of men."

Banneker continued his almanac calculations until his death in 1806. Today all that we have left of his work are his journal and almanacs—and Washington, D.C.

EXPLORE THE IDEA ▼

What kind of mathematics did Banneker use to survey land boundaries? (Hint: See the explanation of how Egyptians redrew farm boundaries on page 10.)

▲▲▲▲▲▲▲▲▲▲

19

Lewis Howard Latimer
(1848–1928)

Inventor

On October 4, 1842, two slaves fled into the night. George and Rebecca Latimer wanted their children born free. Their daring escape took them from Virginia to Massachusetts.

Although Massachusetts had outlawed slavery, George and Rebecca lived in constant fear. Slave owners sometimes placed ads in newspapers, leading to the capture of runaway slaves. In late October, their fears came true. George's owner showed up in Boston to reclaim his "property."

When police arrested George, abolitionists hid Rebecca. **Abolitionists** were people who wanted to abolish, or end, slavery. They fought for George's release. When protests failed, they bought George from his owner and freed him. The Latimer children could grow up free. Lewis Howard Latimer was born in 1848.

In 1863, Latimer watched with envy as his two older brothers signed up to fight in the Civil War. At age 15, he slipped into battle by signing up as a cabin boy on the *U.S.S. Massoit*. The gunboat carried Latimer into action on the James River in Virginia, not far from where his parents had lived as slaves. In 1865, he won an honorable discharge from combat duty.

After the war, Latimer worked for a group of lawyers who handled patents for inventions. A **patent** is a government document that gives an inventor the right to an invention for a limited time. No one can make, use, or sell the invention without the inventor's permission. Each patent application includes a detailed drawing of the invention.

The patent drawings done by mechanical artists fascinated Latimer. He saved his money and bought used drafting tools and books. Night after night, Latimer practiced making drawings. One day, he asked a mechanical artist, "May I do some drawings for you?"

The question opened the door to a new career for Latimer. The artist stared in wonder as Latimer skillfully handled the drafting tools. Latimer impressed his employers so much that they gave him more and more sketches to do. Within 11 years, he became the head mechanical artist at the law firm.

The drawings inspired Latimer to create his own inventions. A short time after he received his first patent, Latimer met another inventor—Alexander Graham Bell. Bell asked Latimer to draw the blueprints for a revolutionary invention called the telephone. In 1876, Latimer's drawings helped Bell win a patent.

Word of Latimer's talents spread. In 1881, he went to work for Hiram Maxim, owner of the United States Electric Company. Maxim wanted to beat Thomas Edison in the race to light up America. Edison had already invented the light bulb. But Maxim wanted to give Americans brighter, longer-lasting bulbs. In 1882, Latimer received a patent for a carbon filament that burned longer than any filament used by Edison. He assigned this patent to Maxim's company.

Edison then tried to get Latimer away from Maxim. He promised Latimer a place in his "idea factory," the nickname for Edison's engineering department. In 1884, Latimer went to work for the Edison Electric Company of New York. Latimer worked there until 1911.

Besides working for Edison, Latimer dedicated his time to helping others. In 1906, he worked in the Henry Street Settlement—a center set up to help people overcome poverty. There Latimer taught English and mechanical drawing to immigrants.

Latimer died in 1928. The Edison Pioneers—a group of scientists who worked with Edison—paid tribute to Latimer at his death.

EXPLORE THE IDEA
▼

Lewis Latimer once wrote: "We create our future by improving present opportunities: however few and small they might be." What does this statement mean? What "few and small" opportunities did Latimer use to create his future?

Mae C. Jemison

Astronaut, Physician

Mae Jemison is truly a world traveler. Not only has she seen Cuba, Kenya, and Thailand from the ground, but she's also seen them from outer space. In 1992, Jemison spent eight days aboard the space shuttle *Endeavour*. She was the first African American woman to orbit the earth.

But her journey into space began long before that. "I recall looking at the stars [as a child], wondering what was up there," Jemison said. "I knew I'd go up there some day, though I didn't know how." Neil Armstrong's walk on the moon during *Apollo 11*'s 1969 flight put a name to Jemison's dream. "I read lots of books about it. I had an encyclopedia about the different phases of Apollo," she recalled. "I don't remember the time I said, 'I want to be an astronaut'; it's just always been there."

Jemison worked hard to make her dream come true. In 1973, when she was just 16, she entered Stanford University in California on a National Achievement Scholarship. To earn a degree in chemical engineering, she had to learn a lot of math, including calculus and statistics. She also studied African and African American history, produced and directed dance and theater productions, and headed the Black Student Union.

After graduating from Stanford, Jemison went to Cornell University Medical College in New York. As a medical student, she worked as a volunteer, traveling to Africa and Asia. After medical school, she joined the Peace Corps. She worked as a doctor in the West African countries of Sierra Leone and Liberia.

In 1985, Dr. Jemison returned to the United States

and took the final step toward her lifelong goal. She applied for the National Aeronautics and Space Administration (NASA) program. In 1987, NASA accepted her into its astronaut training program.

Five years later, during her *Endeavour* space flight, Jemison studied how people move in low gravity. She also explored ways to stop astronauts from getting motion sickness in space. In addition, she calculated how being in the shuttle changed her fellow astronauts' breathing, blood pressure, and heart rates.

On her safe return from space, 10,000 Chicago students gave her a wild welcome back to her hometown. She asked them this question: "When do you think space exploration began?" Some students said 1957, when Russia launched its unmanned satellite called *Sputnik*. Others answered 1969, when the United States launched *Apollo 11*. But Dr. Jemison told the students that they would have to go much further back in history. "People have been exploring space for thousands of years," she said. "When my African ancestors looked up at the sky and began to chart the course of the stars in the heavens, space exploration began. . . . Every people have had their astronomers. The Maya had wonderful astronomers. The Chinese had great astronomers. Every people have had space explorers and mathematicians. Take pride in who you are."

In 1993, Jemison resigned from NASA to practice medicine. She then started her own company, the Jemison Group, which studies advanced technologies. One of its projects is a space-based telecommunications system that helps doctors talk with patients in developing countries.

The Earth We Share is the name of a summer science camp directed by Dr. Jemison for junior high and high school students. They have fun working with mathematics and exploring ideas in science. Some of the students want to be medical doctors. Some of them want to be engineers. But they all know that math is the first step for all of them because mathematics is the language of science.

EXPLORE THE IDEA

Dr. Jemison used mathematics in her work as an astronaut. How is math used in other professions?

Daniel L. Akins

Chemist

Daniel Akins always wanted to know how everything worked. When he was young, he was encouraged to explore the world around him. He was always taking things apart. Luckily, most of the time he could put them back together again. He learned not to be afraid of making mistakes because even his mistakes taught him new things.

In high school, Akins was placed in an honors math program taught by faculty of the University of Miami in Florida. The program introduced him to advanced mathematics. He discovered that this type of math was fun. He thought that this math was like a game because it involved solving mathematical puzzles.

To Akins, solving puzzles was like fixing things, so he put his heart into his math and science courses. He also knew that he would have to get a job when he finished school. He wanted a job that used math and science, so he didn't mind studying hard. He knew that his hard work in school would prepare him for work that he could enjoy for the rest of his life. And he had another reason for working hard in high school: he wanted to go to college.

Akins's hard work paid off. He won a scholarship to Howard University in Washington, D.C. There was a demand for chemists, so he decided to study chemistry. Akins worked hard in college and did well. After graduating from Howard, he went to graduate school at the University of California at Berkeley and earned a Ph.D. in chemistry. A Ph.D. is a Doctor of Philosophy degree. It gave him the title of Dr. Akins.

Dr. Akins then became an associate professor at the University of South Florida in Tampa. After a few years, he left the university and began working for Polaroid. Polaroid needed an experienced chemist like Akins to study dyes used in camera film. Akins enjoyed the experiments that he did on dyes. At Polaroid, Akins was paid more than he received as a college professor. But there were some things that he did not like about this job. He had to work on whatever projects the company wanted. Akins wanted the freedom to choose his own experiments. So, he left Polaroid and became a professor at The City College of New York. He gave up his higher salary, but he could work on projects he found more interesting.

Dr. Akins has advice for young people who are wondering about their futures. He believes that there are many opportunities in mathematics and science. And he repeats what his parents told him: "It pays to work hard in school. It pays off for the rest of your life." That was certainly true for Dr. Daniel Akins.

EXPLORE THE IDEA
▼

If you were in Dr. Akins's place, would you leave Polaroid? Would you choose a job that paid less but let you do more interesting work? Explain.

Math in Real Life: Chemistry

In high school, Daniel Akins studied algebra, geometry, and advanced mathematics. These courses gave him a good understanding of equations. Later, when he studied chemistry, he used algebra to solve chemical equations. So, algebra gave him a good start in chemistry.

Geometry taught Akins to draw diagrams of mathematics problems. In chemistry, he often made diagrams of molecules. The diagrams helped him to see how atoms fit together in a molecule.

Advanced mathematics was a big help, too. It got him ready for calculus. In calculus, you study the pattern of how things change. When Akins was in college, all of his science classes used calculus. Although he didn't know that it would happen this way, the math courses Akins took in high school and college helped to make him an excellent chemist.

25

Portia B. Gordon

Pharmacologist

In high school, Portia Gordon loved mathematics. She says, "I liked using logic to solve problems." She also had fun making up experiments for chemistry. At that time, she did not know that there were many career opportunities for her in science. The only people in science that she knew about were doctors. Because she liked science, she thought about becoming a doctor.

In college, Gordon continued to study mathematics because it was her strongest subject. But when she took chemistry, she discovered she liked it even more than math. Thanks to what she learned in her math classes, she now had a choice of careers. She continued to study mathematics. But she chose chemistry as her major. A **major** is the subject that students spend most of their time studying in college.

Gordon was raised in New York City, and she decided to go to graduate school there. She chose the Albert Einstein School of Medicine at Yeshiva University. She earned a Doctor of Philosophy degree there. This degree gave her the title of Doctor. After graduating, Dr. Gordon stayed at the school's medical center to continue her research. She was given money for a laboratory and was allowed to conduct her own experiments.

Dr. Gordon liked the areas of chemistry that can help cure sick people. This was one reason that she became a pharmacologist. **Pharmacologists** discover new medicines and improve medicines that we already have. Dr. Gordon chose molecular pharmacology. This specific area of pharmacology is the study of medicines to learn how atoms are arranged in molecules. When scientists know the structure of a medicine's molecule, it is possible to make large quantities of a medicine in a factory. Then people can buy medicines at low prices. Lower prices mean that more people can afford to buy the medicines that will help them get well.

Some medicines come from plants. Many were discovered long ago by people in Africa, Asia, and the Americas. But many medicines used today are new. They are created in laboratories. Sometimes a medicine is discovered by accident. For example, a few years ago, bald men were taking a new medicine for high blood pressure. They noticed that new hair was growing on their heads. Doctors were able to prove that the blood pressure medicine made new hair grow for some men. So, by accident, doctors discovered a new use for this medicine.

One way doctors were able to show that this medicine made hair grow was by using statistics. **Statistics** is the study of information that is expressed in numbers. It is a branch of mathematics. Statistics is important in science. Studying numbers can help scientists decide what an experiment really shows. Dr. Gordon's study of mathematics taught her to use statistics. This is one way math helps her in her search for new medicines.

Dr. Gordon has made many important discoveries working with molecules. Sometimes a medicine cures a disease but hurts another part of the body. Changing one molecule in the medicine can sometimes stop the harmful reaction from happening. It may be possible to take the harmful part out, allowing the good part to do its work. Scientists have used this method to make new medicines in laboratories. Dr. Gordon also hopes to make new medicines by changing some old ones. For example, a better understanding of molecules may help pharmacologists find a way to stop the HIV virus from developing into AIDS.

Every summer, Dr. Gordon invites high school students to work in her laboratory. One of her students did such a good job that Dr. Gordon published the information that this student collected. Dr. Gordon hopes that more students will choose careers that make use of mathematics. She says, "More institutions are coming to realize that everyone can make a contribution, no matter who they are."

EXPLORE THE IDEA
▼

Pharmacologists aren't medical doctors, but the work that they do is very important to people's health. In what ways do pharmacologists help people stay healthy and cure sick people of disease?

▲▲▲▲▲▲▲▲▲▲

Michael Spencer
Electrical Engineer

Michael Spencer has always been fascinated with electronics. When he was a child, sometimes neighbors threw out electronic products that were broken. He took them apart to find out how they worked. It was a thrill for him when he could fix a radio or a tape recorder. Even as a child, he believed electronics would be the science of the future. He knew that electronics involved a lot of math. In school, he paid close attention in his math classes. If he did not understand something, he asked questions until the topic became clear. He did not let anything stand in his way. He found math interesting. But he *loved* electronics.

A high school science fair gave Spencer a chance to show what he could do with electronics. For his project, he built equipment to create ultrasonic waves. **Ultrasonic waves** are sound waves that vibrate too fast to be heard by the human ear. An example of ultrasonic sound is a dog whistle. Dogs can hear sounds the whistle makes, but humans cannot.

Spencer did not win the top prize at the science fair. But after the science fair, he knew what he wanted to do with his life. He was going to be an electrical engineer. This goal meant that he needed to learn much more about electronics. It also meant that he would have to go to college.

After receiving his bachelor's degree in engineering from Cornell University, Spencer decided to stay at Cornell. There, he worked for his M.S., or Master of Science, degree in electrical engineering. He was very interested in semiconductors. **Semiconductors** are materials that do not usually conduct, or carry, electricity, but can be *made* to conduct electricity. One semiconductor used in electronics is the transistor.

Spencer also made some important discoveries about solar cells. **Solar cells** absorb sunlight and change it to electricity. These discoveries helped him earn his Ph.D. in electrical engineering.

Dr. Spencer now teaches electrical engineering at Howard University. He also continues to do research on transistors. Through his efforts, Howard University has a Materials Science Research Center of Excellence. Dr. Spencer is the director of this research center. He has also received many other honors. One of them is a Presidential Young Investigator award.

Dr. Spencer has used his knowledge of math and his love of electronics to accomplish a great deal. He also was able to make his dreams come true. When he was told that he might be the only African American electrical engineer, he thought, *Soon there will be many more.* Now, thanks to Dr. Michael Spencer, there are.

EXPLORE THE IDEA
▼

As a child, Michael Spencer decided that electronics was the science of the future. What do you think is the science of the future now? Explain.

Math in Real Life: Electrical Engineering

When most people think of electronics, they think about stereos, TV's, and VCR's. But in factories, electronics is used to control processes and make equipment work properly. Some scientists have called electronics "the science of control."

To prepare for a career in electronics, students need to study mathematics, physics, and chemistry. The high school math courses include algebra, advanced algebra, geometry, pre-calculus, and calculus. Dr. Spencer says that there are many career opportunities in electrical engineering. These opportunities are available not just for the few students with the highest grades. The electronics industry needs anyone who is willing to do good work and who loves electronics.

Evelyn Boyd Granville

Mathematician

Evelyn Granville was born Evelyn Boyd. When Boyd was growing up, many schools were racially segregated. To **segregate** means to keep apart. Many schools with white students did not allow African Americans to attend. Fortunately, Boyd was able to go to Dunbar High School. It was one of the best African American public schools in the country. Students at Dunbar looked up to their teachers. They believed that their teachers were good role models. Boyd liked school, but she could not decide which subject she liked more—math or science.

Boyd's family and teachers encouraged her to study hard and to get good grades in high school. All of her effort was rewarded. She won admission to Smith College in Massachusetts, a well-known school for women. However, this school was expensive. Part of the costs were paid by a scholarship. But her mother and aunt had to make many sacrifices to pay for things the scholarship did not cover. Boyd also worked. She waited on tables and took summer jobs to help pay her way through college.

Boyd graduated *summa cum laude* from Smith College. *Summa cum laude* is Latin for "with the greatest praise." It is a very high honor. She was also accepted at Yale University. At Yale, she earned a M.A., or Master of Arts degree, in mathematics and physics.

In 1949, Boyd earned her Ph.D. in mathematics. She was the first African American woman to earn this degree at Yale University. Boyd and Margaret Lee Browne were the first two African American women in the nation to earn Ph.D.'s in mathematics. It would be another ten years before other African American women followed in their footsteps. Today many more African American men and women have Ph.D.'s in mathematics. Two of them were Boyd's students at Fisk University in Tennessee.

When Boyd first received her Ph.D., jobs were difficult for her to get. She faced discrimination because of her race and because she was a woman. For 16 years, Boyd worked for the U.S. government and for private companies. She used her knowledge of mathematics to solve many difficult problems for her employers. Then she got an unexpected chance to do something that she'd always wanted to do.

When she was a college student at Smith, Boyd became fascinated with astronomy. Astronomy is the study of the stars and the universe. When the United States began its space program, jobs were offered to mathematicians who wanted to work in astronomy. This job combined two subjects that Boyd enjoyed. She became part of the space program. One of her contributions to the U.S. space effort was finding better ways to map orbits. **Orbits** are the paths of planets and moons moving in space. She also worked on the Project Vanguard and Project Mercury space probes.

In addition to her work for the space program, Boyd worked for IBM as a senior mathematician and computer expert. Then she became a professor at California State University in Los Angeles. Part of her job there was to work with elementary and high school students to find better ways to teach mathematics.

In 1970, Evelyn Boyd married Edward V. Granville. When she thinks about her past, Evelyn Boyd Granville considers herself lucky. She once said, "I feel that I have had a very rich life." Many people dream of finding work that they enjoy and that also helps others. Evelyn Boyd Granville has found that kind of work. Her life is proof that math opens many career doors.

EXPLORE THE IDEA
▼

What part of Evelyn Boyd Granville's life do you find the most impressive? Why?

▲▲▲▲▲▲▲▲▲▲▲

Hubert K. Rucker

Physiologist

Hubert Rucker directed the medical technology clinics at Children's Hospital in Washington, D.C., for 17 years. A **medical technician** uses special equipment to test a person's state of health. Have you ever had blood drawn from your body for medical tests? The person who took your blood was probably a medical technician. Blood and other body fluids reveal a lot of information about your health. Doctors use this information to help them decide how to treat patients.

Hubert Rucker earned a Bachelor of Science, or B.S., degree from Texas Southern University in Houston. When he graduated from college, he had a choice of many jobs. He chose the job at Children's Hospital because it would give him valuable experience. It also allowed him to help people. Being a medical technician is one of the most important jobs in a hospital. But that was not enough for Rucker. He had a lot of ideas for better ways to run hospital laboratories. To get the chance to use these ideas, he needed to learn more. So Rucker went back to school at Howard University's graduate school. He could only attend part-time because he also had to work. But there was an advantage to keeping his job at the hospital. It taught him things he was not learning in school.

Rucker was deeply interested in physiology. **Physiology** is the study of how living things work. After many years of working and going to school, Rucker finally earned his Ph.D. in physiology.

After finishing graduate school, Dr. Rucker began research on Alzheimer's disease. Alzheimer's is a condition that causes loss of memory, especially in older people. To find a cure, doctors need to know more about how the brain works. One area scientists are learning more about are brain neurotransmitters. **Neurotransmitters** are chemicals that carry messages from the brain to other parts of the body. These chemicals have a lot to do with how the brain works. Scientists believe that when the brain does not work correctly, there is either too much or too little of some of these chemicals. Dr. Rucker is studying a special kind of neurotransmitter that helps the brain locate the direction of sounds.

In 1985, Dr. Rucker became a professor of physiology at Meharry Medical College in Nashville, Tennessee. Many African American medical doctors have graduated from Meharry. He also works with high school students who attend a special program at Meharry on Saturdays and during the summer. The students in this program are seeing for themselves how important studying mathematics can be.

EXPLORE THE IDEA
▼▼▼

Hubert Rucker had a bachelor's degree that enabled him to get a good job that paid well. Even so, he decided to earn another degree. Why do you think he did this? Would you have made the same decision?

Math in Real Life: Physiology

Mathematics gave Hubert Rucker many tools that he needed for his work in physiology. For example, Dr. Rucker's work makes use of statistics. Statistics is a branch of mathematics. Statistics is the study of information that is expressed in numbers. It is used by every scientist. Dr. Rucker uses statistics to help him understand his experiments.

When an experiment is finished, the measurements from it are arranged in tables. A scientist then asks a lot of questions. Is the experiment showing a definite result? Does the experiment prove anything? The answers to these questions come partly from looking at statistics, measurements, tables, and graphs. Statistics helps scientists find the answers they're looking for. Statistics also helps them make important decisions about what other experiments are needed.

Norma Merrick Sklarek

Architect

Norma Merrick Sklarek [SKLAH-rehk] was always interested in the spaces created by buildings. Today she is an architect. An **architect** designs buildings. Sklarek thinks architects should improve people's **environment**, or surroundings, wherever they are. Being an architect has given her an opportunity to make a difference in the ways people live.

Architecture combines two of Sklarek's strongest subjects in school—art and math, including algebra and geometry. She went to college at Columbia University's School of Architecture in New York City.

When Sklarek first became an architect, it was difficult for her to get a job. People did not want to hire her because she was African American and because she was a woman. She went to 19 companies for interviews. At the twentieth place, she finally got her first job as an architect. But there were things that she didn't like about the job. They did not give her a chance to do important work. She was not getting the experience that she wanted. She had to deal with discrimination by her employer.

Later, she said that if something starts out hard, she works even harder. Then she does more than catch up. She moves ahead. This stick-with-it spirit has put her at the top of her field. For 17 years, Sklarek was the head of a department at an important architectural company. Later, she became the first woman vice-president at another well-known architectural firm. Sklarek has also owned her own company.

A career in architecture has given Sklarek the chance to create beautiful buildings. She has designed many kinds of buildings, from small homes to huge office towers. Terminal One at the Los Angeles International Airport is one of her biggest design projects. Sklarek is the only woman member of the Los Angeles Chapter of the American Institute of Architects to win the special award of Fellow. She won this award for her outstanding work.

Sklarek was the first African American woman to get an architect's license in New York. (Architects must be licensed by the state.) She was also the first African American woman to get a license in California. Now, Sklarek speaks to groups of young people who are going to take the architectural licensing test. She says many more African American architects are needed.

EXPLORE THE IDEA
▼

Take a really good look at some of the buildings in your community. Choose one that you would want to change if you could. How would you change it?

Math in Real Life: Architecture

Architects use basic principles of mathematics. Drawing a blueprint requires the use of ratios and proportions. Geometry is a basic part of architecture.

Architects must know about the strengths of materials to make sure that the structure is safe and will stand up to weather and earthquakes. Sometimes architects remodel homes. If the wrong wall is removed, the roof may fall in. So the study of architecture also includes learning about holding up heavy loads. This is a branch of physics that also requires a lot of math, including calculus. Students who take four years of math in high school will be prepared to take many subjects in college. Some will decide, like Norma Merrick Sklarek, to make architecture their career.

Roosevelt Gentry

Biomathematician

It was not always clear that Roosevelt Gentry would become a mathematician. He always loved math but he loved biology, too. He knew that he could find a job in biology. But he wasn't sure if he could find work in mathematics. One event that helped Gentry to make up his mind was a note he received when he was in high school.

The note was written in his yearbook. It was from a math teacher whom Gentry respected. It said, "Roosevelt can do anything he wants to do in life." Dr. Gentry says this message changed the direction of his life. It gave him the encouragement and confidence he needed to choose math as his major subject in college. He selected biology as his minor subject.

After four years at Jackson State University, in Mississippi, Gentry was awarded a B.S., a Bachelor of Science degree, in mathematics. Gentry then attended graduate school at Rutgers University in New Jersey, where he earned his Ph.D. at the age of 26. After he received his Ph.D., Gentry had many possible career opportunities. He decided to teach mathematics at Jackson State University.

Soon after Dr. Gentry began teaching at Jackson State, he became chairperson of the department. He was very busy, but he still found time to write books on mathematics and psychology. He has also written computer software for kindergarten through college mathematics courses.

Throughout his career, Dr. Gentry has been involved in many different aspects of the mathematics field. For example, he was invited to give presentations at the first U.S./Russian Joint Mathematics conference in Russia. He was also selected as a finalist (4 out of 450 mathematicians) world-wide for an International Prize in mathematics.

What he has always wanted to do, though, was work in biomathematics. **Biomathematics** combines math and biology. These were the two subjects Dr. Gentry enjoyed the most. He wanted to use mathematics to solve problems in biology.

Dr. Gentry's wish came true when he won a Minority Research Initiative grant. A **grant** is an award of money that pays for someone to study a specific topic or subject. Gentry uses his grant to do experiments in biology on a computer. First, he makes a mathematical model of an experiment. Then the computer solves the equations.

More and more, experiments are tried first with computer models. Some experiments cannot be done in real life. For example, how will a new virus attack the human body? This experiment can't be tried with a real person because it is too dangerous. But a model shows what *might* happen. Scientists can create various models for an experiment. The models can be viewed on a computer screen. Then scientists try to decide which model's result is most likely to occur.

Even though he is a busy man, Dr. Gentry spends a lot of time talking to high school students about careers in mathematics. He tells them that math can open many doors. He also tells students that a career in mathematics can mean more than a chance to earn a good salary and to have steady work. It is also a chance to do something you love and to accomplish important things. Dr. Gentry hopes that more young people will follow his example and earn a degree in an area that he loves—mathematics.

EXPLORE THE IDEA

▼

Can you think of some experiments that are too dangerous to do except as computer models? What are they?

▲▲▲▲▲▲▲▲▲▲
▼▲▼▲▼▲▼▲▼▲

Mathematics and You

It is never too early to plan for the future. The people featured in the biographies started planning for their futures early in life. They discovered early on that mathematics was their gateway to exciting careers. Now it is time for you to plan for your future. In this section, you will learn the ways in which math can enhance your interests and natural talents and lead you into higher-paying careers.

Everyone can succeed in math. You will see in this section that you use math every day. It's a natural part of daily life. You will also learn that math is not only about numbers. It is also about ideas and recognizing patterns. You will also discover how math can be fun.

Finally, you will read about the math classes that are offered throughout your school career. As you read this section, think about how these courses can help you reach your goals and dreams and help you to make intelligent choices for your future.

▲ *An IBM technician assembles a complex computer part at a manufacturing plant.*

▲ *Using her strong math and computer science background, Donna Auguste invented a new way to compose music on computers.*

In the first part of this book, you learned the history of mathematics. In the second part, you read about several African Americans who have excelled in the fields of math and science. Now it's time to think about how you might take part in continuing the rich heritage of mathematics.

Students often ask: "What's the use of mathematics? Why should I study it?" Here's one good reason that may catch your attention: *Math makes money*. It can be your key to a well-paying career and a comfortable lifestyle.

A second reason is that mathematics can be *fun*. It can provide lively exercise for your mind, just as sports provide exercise for your body.

EDUCATION AND YOUR FUTURE

Fifty years ago, a person with a high school diploma could usually count on finding a decent-paying job. This is no longer true. In your lifetime, three out of every four new jobs will require at least some college. For people who do not finish high school, there will be *very* few jobs—and these jobs will pay very low wages.

Look at the bar graph on page 40. Each bar stands for a different level of education. It shows the average pay that a person with each level of education earned in 1990.

The graph shows how education increases earning power. For example, in 1990, the average college graduate earned over $15,000 more than the average high school dropout. Over 30 years, that would amount to a difference of more than $450,000!

WHY MATHEMATICS?

It's easy to understand how more schooling can lead to better-paying jobs. But how can *studying* mathematics raise your earning power?

There are several ways. Mathematical skills are the key to jobs in technology and science. These skills

EXPLORE THE IDEA

What well-paying jobs can you think of that might require a strong background in math?

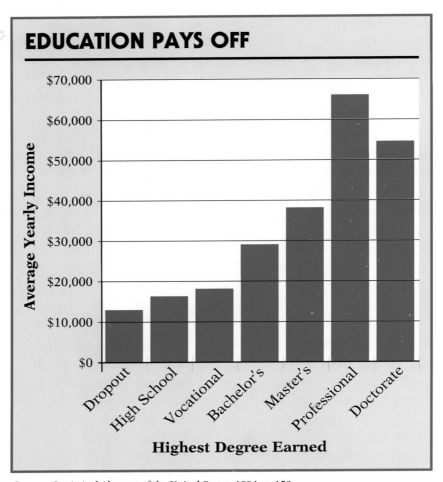

EDUCATION PAYS OFF

Average Yearly Income vs. Highest Degree Earned

Source: *Statistical Abstract of the United States,* 1994, p. 158

are needed for well-paying jobs, such as sound engineers, video-tape operators, opticians, and laboratory technicians. Math skills are also useful in working with computers. Knowing how to use computers is a requirement for two out of every three new jobs today. Computers are even needed for careers in baseball, football, and track. For example, successful coaches use computers to analyze athletes' performances and to plot winning strategies.

Mathematical thinking can help you in almost *any* career. Employers know that if you are mathematically skilled, you are likely to do well in new situations. They know that they can count on you to think logically and to solve job-related problems.

▲ *above: Daniel Akins, chemist, at the City College of New York. right top: Mae C. Jemison, NASA astronaut. right bottom: Michael Spencer, electrical engineer, at Howard University.*

A recent government study found this simple fact: *The more college mathematics courses you take, the greater your earning potential will be.*

Even many jobs that don't require a college degree require mathematical thinking. Take toll collection, for example. In many cities, to get a job as a bridge or tunnel toll collector, you must pass a written test. Many questions on these tests require people to know and use math.

YOU USE MATHEMATICS ALL THE TIME

Everyone uses mathematics. It's a part of your everyday life. You use math when you read a table in a newspaper. You use math when you shop. You use math when you cook, dance, or play games of chance. You even use mathematical thinking in sports and in creating and designing artwork.

EXPLORE THE IDEA ▼

How do the people in these pictures use mathematics in their work?

▲▲▲▲▲▲▲▲▲

Are you surprised? You may think that mathematics is about numbers. In fact, it is mostly about ideas. It's about patterns. The patterns that we use when we calculate with numbers are only one such set of ideas.

Here is an example: Imagine that the patterns on this page are staircases. Each staircase is made of square tiles. The one-step staircase uses one tile. Every other staircase uses an increasing number of tiles.

Number of Stairs	Number of Tiles
1	1
2	3
3	6
4	10
5	15
6	21

1 step   2 steps   3 steps   4 steps   5 steps   6 steps

The table shows the number of tiles in each staircase. Can you see any patterns? (*Hint:* Look at the second column. Note the difference between each pair of neighboring numbers.)

Think of a staircase with seven steps. How many tiles would it use? How many are needed for 10 steps? Architects, artists, builders, and interior designers work with mathematical patterns all the time.

A great deal of mathematical thinking is about finding and using patterns. Medical researchers study patterns in people's medical histories and in data gathered from tests. For example, Dr. Clarice D. Reid is a famous researcher of sickle cell anemia. The patterns that she discovered in patients' symptoms and responses to certain medications have helped her teach doctors and nurses how to care for patients with this disease.

In addition, geologists study patterns in rocks to discover the natural history of an area. Musicians often use patterns of sound to create music. Business experts study people's buying patterns to decide where to place a new store.

EXPLORE THE IDEA ▼

Hypatia, a mathematician who taught in Egypt around the year 400 CE, wrote about the staircase pattern. She called the numbers in the tile column *triangular numbers*. Can you guess why?

All your life, you have looked for mathematical patterns to answer your questions about how things work. For example, figuring out bus or train schedules and estimating your walking speed help you to know when to leave your house to arrive at a station on time.

▲ *As a recording engineer, this young man uses his understanding of mathematical patterns to help him work with sound in the studio.*

Mathematics for fun

Exercising your mind can be the most enjoyable use of mathematics. It's something that you can do by yourself or with friends. The staircase problem previously described is an example of "mental sport." Following are a few others:

The Game of Nim In this game, 20 stones or counters are placed on a table. You and another player take turns removing some of the stones. You may take either one, two, or three stones at a turn. The person who takes the last stone loses. If you go first, how can you be sure to win?

Crossing the River This puzzle is a favorite of the Kpelle people of Liberia, a country in western Africa.

A man has a leopard, a goat, and a bunch of cassava leaves. He wants to get them across a river, but his boat is only big enough to carry one item at a time. If he leaves the leopard and the goat together, the leopard will eat the goat. If he leaves the goat and the cassava leaves together, the goat will eat the leaves. How does he get everything safely across the river?

The Nine Coins A queen has nine coins. They look exactly alike. Eight of the coins are made of gold. The ninth coin is a fake. It weighs slightly less than one of the gold coins. The queen has a scale. How can she find out which coin is the fake with only two weighings?

▲ *African mathematical games are played all over the world, including the United States. Ntchuba is a board game of strategy.*

STUDYING MATHEMATICS IN HIGH SCHOOL

In high school, it is important that you choose your math courses wisely. Some people might tell you to take easy math classes. Often these classes are called "general math" or "consumer math." This is not good advice. These classes can often lead to a dead end. They will not help your future.

The classes that you need to take are academic math classes. In these courses, you will explore concepts in algebra, geometry, statistics and probability, logic, and calculus. Academic math courses are the "gatekeeper" courses. Students who don't take them are turned away at the gate of higher learning. Admission to most colleges requires three years of academic math classes. You will also need these classes to get and keep a well-paying job. Understanding advanced math is an important factor in qualifying for jobs in science and technology.

Pre-algebra and *algebra* are the first math courses offered in most high schools. When you study algebra, you learn how to set up and use mathematical expressions to describe real-life situations and to solve problems about them. Algebra is often taught in a two-year sequence.

In *geometry*, you study about lines and shapes and how they relate to each other and to the real world. You learn how they are used in such areas as art, construction, engineering, and sports. Geometry also teaches you how to use logical reasoning to solve problems beyond the world of mathematics.

Trigonometry is taught sometimes as part of an advanced algebra course and sometimes as a separate course. It deals with relationships among the sides and angles of triangles. Trigonometry is used in such areas as astronomy, navigation, and engineering.

Some students take *pre-calculus* and/or *calculus* after they've studied algebra and geometry. Calculus deals with such topics as motion and rate of change.

Algebra, geometry, algebra II, and trigonometry are often required courses for admission into college. In addition, they are important courses that will help you learn how math can be applied to various careers and to many aspects of your daily life.

Many of these areas of mathematics come from the rich heritage of Africa. The first book on algebra appeared in Egypt around 1700 BCE. The Egyptians used geometry to replace farm boundaries washed away by the Nile. The pyramids could not have been built without an understanding of trigonometry.

▲ *This math teacher helps his students prepare for future careers in science and technology by teaching them advanced mathematics.*

EXPLORE THE IDEA ▼

How can you give yourself the best chance of doing well in math classes?

▲▲▲▲▲▲▲▲▲▲

MATHEMATICS: A HUMAN ACTIVITY

There is no magic to doing well in mathematics. It's largely a matter of recognizing patterns and the connections among them. It doesn't necessarily take special talent, but it does take determination and perseverance. You must stick with it.

It takes work, too. It's important to stay focused in your math classes and to be observant. Don't be afraid to ask questions or to discuss your reasoning with others. Use opportunities to solve mathematical puzzles and play mathematical games. You can have fun while you're learning.

You will find the effort well worth it. Taking math will help you manage your money and make wise financial decisions. Through mathematics, you can expand your range of career choices and build a richer, more secure future. Knowing math will help you better understand important economic issues. You will better understand news that is expressed in terms of numbers. It will make you a better citizen, one who is able to decide what is true and what is false. Understanding math will help you make intelligent choices for yourself, your family, and your community.

AFRICA TODAY

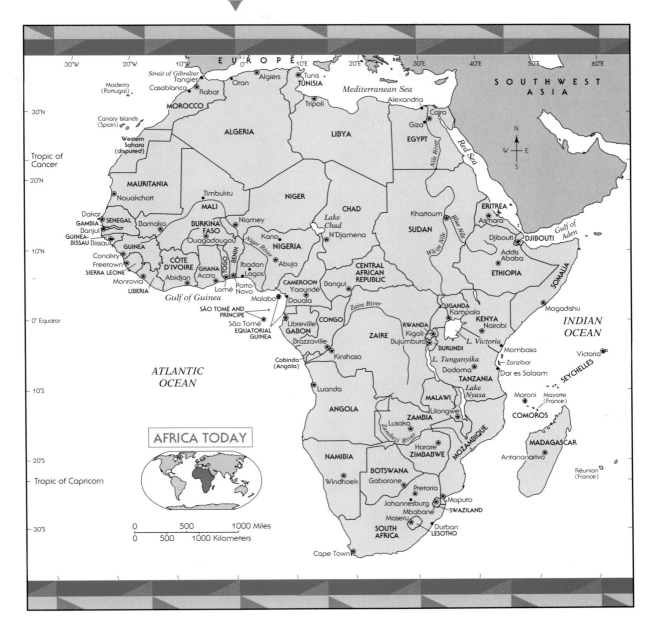

AFRICA TODAY

0   500   1000 Miles
0   500   1000 Kilometers

GLOSSARY

abolitionists people who wanted to end slavery (page 20)

almanacs books that forecast weather, as well as moon, sun, and tide movements (page 19)

architect a person who designs buildings and other structures (page 34)

biomathematics a science that combines math and biology (page 37)

coordinates numbers that locate a point on a line, on a plane, or in a space (page 10)

environment a surrounding (page 34)

geometry mathematics that deals with points, lines, planes, and shapes and their measurement and relationships in space (page 10)

grant an award of money that pays for someone to study a specific topic or subject (page 37)

major the subject that students spend most of their time studying in college (page 26)

mathematics the use of numbers, patterns, and shapes to describe and explain the world (page 6)

medical technician someone who uses special equipment to test a person's state of health (page 32)

neurotransmitters chemicals that carry messages from the brain to other parts of the body (page 33)

orbits the paths of planets and moons moving in space (page 31)

patent a government document that gives an inventor the right to an invention for a limited time (page 20)

pharmacologists people who discover new medicines and improve medicines that already exist (page 26)

physiology the study of how living things work (page 32)

pyramid a structure with a square base and four triangular sides that meet at a point (page 10)

segregate to separate or keep apart (page 30)

semiconductors materials that do not usually conduct electricity, but can be made to carry electricity (page 28)

solar cells cells that absorb sunlight and change it to electricity (page 29)

statistics the study of information that is expressed in numbers (page 27)

surveyor a person who measures the size, shape, and boundaries of a piece of land with special equipment (page 19)

tallies marks that represent number counts (page 6)

ultrasonic waves sound waves that vibrate too fast to be heard by the human ear (page 28)